JULES FEIFFER

contributed his first strip to New York's *Village Voice* some eight years ago. Today his work appears in over forty newspapers, *Playboy* magazine, the *New Republic*, the *Paris Herald Tribune* and the *London Observer*.

He has also illustrated a children's book and written a one-act play, which had its world premiere at Gian Carlo Menotti's Festival of Two Worlds at Spoleto. His cartoon short, *Munro*, won the Academy Award. His first novel, *Harry, the Rat with Women*, was published in the summer of 1963.

Mr. Feiffer's *Sick, Sick, Sick; Boy, Girl. Boy, Girl.*; and *The Explainers* are published in Signet editions.

Published by The New American Library

hold me!

JULES FEIFFER

A SIGNET BOOK

Published as a SIGNET BOOK
by arrangement with Random House, Inc.,
who have authorized this softcover edition.

First Printing, July, 1964

The author wishes to thank The Hall Syndicate, Inc., *The Village
Voice, Playboy* magazine, *New Republic* and *The London Observer* for
permission to reprint the strips in this book.

SIGNET TRADEMARK REG. U.S. PAT. OFF. AND FOREIGN COUNTRIES
REGISTERED TRADEMARK — MARCA REGISTRADA
HECHO EN CHICAGO, U.S.A.

SIGNET BOOKS are published by
The New American Library of World Literature, Inc.
501 Madison Avenue, New York, New York 10022

PRINTED IN THE UNITED STATES OF AMERICA

ALL MY LIFE
I'VE FELT THAT
DEEP WITHIN
ME I'VE BEEN
SUPPRESSING
A GREAT
EVIL.

THAT'S WHY
I WAS
AFRAID
WHEN MOTHER
HAD MY
PORTRAIT
PAINTED.

 BUT MY PORTRAIT
MADE ME LOOK
YOUNG AND
GOOD AND
INNOCENT.
IT REMINDED
ME OF THAT
STORY - **YOU
REMEMBER** -
" THE PORTRAIT
OF DORIAN
GRAY —

 ... WHERE THIS
YOUNG MAN
WITH GREAT
EVIL IN HIM
NEVER AGED
A DAY - BUT
HIS **PORTRAIT**
GREW OLD AND
UGLY AND
EVIL.

 SO I **HID** MY PORTRAIT DETERMINED **NEVER** TO LOOK AT IT AGAIN. AND AS THE YEARS WENT BY, I WENT TO WORK, I CAME HOME, I WENT TO WORK, I CAME HOME. BUT I DID NOT AGE A DAY.

 I **CRINGED** AT WHAT MY PORTRAIT MUST LOOK LIKE. I GOT MARRIED, I WENT TO WORK, I CAME HOME. I HAD CHILDREN, I WENT TO WORK, I CAME HOME. BUT I DID NOT AGE A DAY.

FINALLY I COULD
STAND IT **NO LONGER!**
I **HAD** TO KNOW
MY **REAL** SOUL
AND IT WAS ON
THAT CANVAS! I
RIPPED THE
PAINTING FROM
ITS HIDING PLACE
AND **REMOVED**
THE COVER!

IT
WAS
BLANK.

I BURNED
THE CANVAS
BUT IT
MADE NO
DIFFERENCE.
I DID NOT
AGE A
DAY.

I JUST
GO TO
WORK
AND I
COME
HOME

IF YOU DON'T HAVE ANY RESPECT FOR **YOURSELF** THEN IN TIME YOU'LL FORCE **ME** TO LOSE RESPECT FOR YOU. IF **I** LOSE RESPECT FOR YOU I'LL **WANT** TO LEAVE YOU. ARGH— YOU'RE PLEATING MY SHIRT, DOLLY.

BUT WITH A **LOOSER** HOLD— YOU FREE TO GO **YOUR** WAY, I FREE TO GO **MINE**— WE'LL BE **SO MUCH** HAPPIER. TRY TO SEE IT **MY** WAY, DOLLY.

ME FREE TO GO MY WAY?

I USED TO WORK FOR
THE F.B.I. - ASSIGNED
TO THE PEACE
MOVEMENT-
UNDERGROUND
AGENT TO
CHECK
OUT
COMMUNIST
INFILTRATION

ALL PRETTY ROUTINE-
MASS MEETINGS -
PICKETING THE
WHITE HOUSE-
JOHNSON
SHAKING
HANDS,
NO RESULTS
WHATEVER -

THEN I MET EDNA-
SOFT- COMPELLING-
DOCTRINAIRE-
SHE FELL IN
LOVE. I FELL
IN LOVE. WE
DECIDED
ON
MARRIAGE

BUT MY SECRET SEPARATED
US. I HAD TO TELL HER.
I PROCEEDED TO DO
SO. ON OUR WEDDING
NIGHT I REPORTED
"EDNA, I AM AN
UNDERGROUND.
AGENT FOR
YOUR F.B.I.

EDNA WEPT. THEN SHE TOLD
ME **HER** SECRET. "SAM"
SHE REPORTED, "I AM
AN UNDERGROUND
COMMUNIST
ASSIGNED TO
INFILTRATE THE
PEACE
MOVEMENT.

YOU CAN IMAGINE WHAT FOLLOWED. A LOVERS QUARREL. I INSISTED EDNA GIVE UP **HER** WORK. SHE INSISTED I GIVE UP **MINE**

WE CONSULTED A MARRIAGE COUNSELOR. HE ADVISED US TO COMPROMISE— "ALL FORMS OF EXTREMISM ARE MISGUIDED" HE REPORTED. "QUIT YOUR RESPECTIVE JOBS AND JOIN A COMMUNITY CENTER"

I COULDN'T EDNA COULDN'T. WE SAID GOOD-BYE AND I TURNED HER IN

WHAT I SAY IS
BLA BLA BLA—
WHAT I MEAN
IS BEAUTY
AND POETRY.

WHAT I SAY IS
GIBBLE GABBLE GIBBLE—
WHAT I MEAN IS
I AM A LOST SOUL.
STUDY MY HAUNTED
EYES.

WHAT I SAY IS
HA HA HA HA –
WHAT I MEAN
IS LIFE IS A
WASTE AND
NOBODY CARES
A **FIG** FOR ME.

SOMEDAY I'LL MEET A
MAN WHO WILL IGNORE
MY STUPID WORDS AND
KNOW INSTANTLY THE
FRAGILE, DELICATE,
PERFECTION THAT
LIES BEHIND THEM.

HE WILL SEE
THROUGH ME.
AND OURS
WILL BE A
BEAUTIFUL
LOVE —

I'LL
HURT
HIM.

IF YOU WOULD LIKE TO LEAVE A MESSAGE PLEASE WAIT TILL YOU HEAR THE SIGNAL ON THIS RECORDING. YOU HAVE THIRTY SECONDS.

SYLVIA?.

BEEP

SYLVIATHISISBERNARDHONEYIMSORRY - ABOUTWHATISAIDBELIEVEMEICOULD - CUTMYTONGUEOUTIKNOWISAIDI'DNEVER - APOLOGIZEBUTICANTLIVEWITHOUTYOU - DOYOUUNDERSTANDIWASWRONGSOWRONG - ILOVEYOULOVEYOULOVE —

IT DIDN'T SEEM
LIKE THIRTY
SECONDS.

I'M SORRY, SIR. WE ARE NOT A REAL ESTATE COMPANY. WE ARE A TELEPHONE COMPANY.

BUT THAT'S WHAT I WANT TO RENT— A TELEPHONE BOOTH. A **SIDEWALK GLASS** TELEPHONE BOOTH.

CAN'T YOU RECEIVE YOUR CALLS **INDOORS**, SIR? WE HAVE **MANY** ATTRACTIVE VARI-COLORED **PRIVATE** PHONES—

NOBODY EVER **CALLS** ME INDOORS! PEOPLE THINK **I'M** ALOOF! I GIVE THE WRONG **IMPRESSION!** IF I STAY COOPED UP IN A CLOSED APARTMENT, HOW WILL THEY EVER KNOW I'M OPEN TO FRIENDSHIP? BUT IF I MOVED INTO A PUBLIC TELEPHONE BOOTH—

ISN'T THAT WHAT I CALL A COINCIDENCE. I WROTE YOU JUST YESTERDAY — FINE, WE'RE ALL FINE. WELL, YOU SHOULDN'T HAVE WORRIED.
WHO'S ON THE PHONE?

WELL, IT'S A LITTLE HARD TO TALK RIGHT NOW, MOTHER. RUTH AND I ARE HAVING ONE OF OUR WHAT I CALL DIFFERENCES OF OPINION.
MARVIN, WHO'S ON THE PHONE?

MARVIN. WHO I HAVE ASKED YOU IS IT?
NO, MOTHER. NOTHING TO WORRY ABOUT. I KNOW YOU TOLD ME WHAT TO EXPECT. I KNOW SHE NEEDS FIRM HANDLING.

MARVIN!
HONEST, MOTHER, IT'S BEST YOU DON'T TALK TO HER. YOU KNOW HOW YOU TWO GO AT EACH OTHER- SURE, MOTHER, I REALIZE SHE STARTS IT.

I USED TO BE VERY ATHLETIC— A **MODEL** OF AMERICAN YOUTH!

BUT **THEN** CAME THE **CONGO** CRISIS WHEN IT SEEMED THAT WAR WAS **INEVITABLE.** MY **EYES** STARTED BOTHERING ME AND I HAD TO GIVE UP READING THE PAPERS AND GET **GLASSES.**

BUT EXCEPT FOR MY EYES I WAS **STILL** IN PRETTY GOOD SHAPE — AND THEN CAME THE **LAOTIAN** CRISIS. IT SEEMED THAT WAR WAS **INEVITABLE.** MY HEARING STARTED BOTHERING ME AND I HAD TO GIVE UP LISTENING TO RADIO NEWS AND GET A **HEARING** AID.

BUT OUTSIDE OF BUMPING INTO THINGS AND NEVER QUITE KNOWING WHAT WAS GOING ON I WAS **STILL** IN **FAIRLY** GOOD SHAPE. AND THEN CAME THE **BERLIN** CRISIS. MY BACK GAVE OUT. MY STOMACH TURNED SOUR. AND I DEVELOPED **MIGRAINE.**

THEN I HEARD SOMEWHERE THAT CRITICS WERE ATTACK-ING AMERICAN YOUTH FOR BEING OUT OF SHAPE —

I CAN'T **SEE** —
I CAN'T **HEAR** —
I CAN'T **BREATHE** —
I CAN'T **STAND** —
AND I DON'T WANT ANYTHING MORE THAN TO GO INTO A FALLOUT SHELTER AND **VANISH** —

WHAT DO THEY
MEAN OUT OF
SHAPE? I LOOK
UPON MYSELF
AS THE MAN OF
THE FUTURE.

MY WIFE AND I
HAD BROKEN UP,
MY JOB WAS
GOING DOWN
THE DRAIN AND
I WAS DE-
VELOPING A
DRINKING
PROBLEM. I
SAW MYSELF
AS A LATENT
FAILURE.

SO ONE DAY I SAT
DOWN AND ASKED
MYSELF **WHY**.
AN INTELLIGENT
MAN SHOULD
BE ABLE TO
WORK THROUGH
HIS
PROBLEMS.

THE FIRST ANSWER I CAME UP WITH WAS THE ARMS RACE, THE BERLIN CRISIS AND THE FEAR OF OVER-POPULATION. BUT I FELT THAT, WHILE TRUE, THIS WAS BASICALLY AN **EVASION**.

MY SECOND ANS-WER WAS THAT IT WAS A PLOT ON THE PART OF MY ENEMIES TO CRUSH ME BECAUSE OF MY BEING SO BRIGHT. WHILE NO DOUBT IN PART TRUE, I FELT THAT THIS **TOO** WAS AN EVASION.

THEN I HIT ON
THE ANSWER
I'D BEEN
AVOIDING ALL
ALONG. THE
ROOT OF MY
FAILURE LAY
IN MY UNHAPPY
CHILDHOOD.

SO I WENT INTO
ANALYSIS AND
FOUND OUT
THAT I HAD
A VERY
HAPPY
CHILDHOOD.

THEREFORE, CONSIDERING MY BACKGROUND, MY INTELLECT AND MY ABILITY TO SEE THROUGH MY OWN EVASIONS AS EVIDENCE, I PROVED TO MYSELF THAT DESPITE MINOR SETBACKS I WAS **MISTAKEN** IN MY PREVIOUS SELF-ANALYSIS. I WAS **NOT** A FAILURE!

RESEARCH PROVES I'M A **SUCCESS!**

A TOASHT!

HELLO? MR. MILES TOOMUCH, THE JAZZ
MUSICIAN? THIS IS THE **STATE DEPT.-
BUREAU OF IMAGES** - VICTOR VENEER
SPEAKING. I'M CALLING, SIR, IN REGARD
TO THE ATTORNEY GENERAL'S
PLAN FOR IMPROVING OUR
IMAGE ABROAD BY SENDING
OVER OUR INTELLECTUAL
AND ARTISTIC **ELITE** -
OH, YES, YOU ARE, MR.
TOOMUCH! - WELL,
WE SAY SO!

ANYHOW, WE DOWN HERE AT **IMAGE** JUST
WANTED TO CHECK YOU OUT ON SOME
DIFFICULT QUESTIONS YOU MIGHT BE
ASKED ON YOUR TRIP- YOU KNOW-
BY RIOTING STUDENTS OR
SOMETHING.
FOR INSTANCE WHAT WOULD
YOU SAY ABOUT OUR
RESUMPTION OF ATMOS-
PHERIC TESTING?

OH, YOU'D SAY **THAT** WOULD YOU? AND
HOW WOULD YOU HANDLE DIVISIVE
QUESTIONS ON RACE RELATIONS?—
I SEE—. AND ABOUT OUR BERLIN,
NATO AND ASIAN POLICIES?—
—MMM - HMMMM-

WELL, MR. TOOMUCH,
INSTEAD OF ALL
THAT COULDN'T
YOU JUST PLAY
SOMETHING ON
YOUR HORN?

I MEAN
ISN'T **MUSIC**
TRULY THE
BEST
COMMUNICATOR?

HEAVENS, **NO** ONE IS TRYING TO SUPPRESS YOU, MR TOOMUCH, BUT IT **IS** SORT OF **YOUR** IMAGE OF OUR IMAGE AGAINST **OUR** IMAGE OF OUR IMAGE, ISN'T IT? AND SHOULDN'T IMPORTANT DECISIONS ON IMAGE BE LEFT IN THE HANDS OF THE PUBLIC RELATIONS EXPERTS WHO MAY HAVE ACCESS TO CLASSIFIED PUBLICITY THAT YOU DON'T KNOW ABOUT?

WELL, LOOK, MR. TOOMUCH, BEFORE WE REISSUE YOU YOUR PASSPORT WHY DON'T I SEND YOU OUR SAMPLE IMAGE SALES KIT, INCLUDING PAMPHLETS, FILM STRIPS AND VISUAL AIDS - ALL UNDER THE GENERAL TITLE OF "OPERATION: GOOD GUY." WE'D LIKE YOU TO HAVE THE RIGHT SLANT BEFORE YOU WENT ABROAD, SIR.

AFTER ALL IMAGE
IS EVERYBODY'S
JOB.

ONCE AGAIN FROM THE SUB·SUB BASEMENT OF THE TIME·LIFE BUILDING IN LITTLE OLD NEW YORK, CLUB MEGATON, THE **FUN** FALLOUT SHELTER BRINGS YOU THAT EVER-SAFE SINGER OF SONGS · CLYDE **CONELRAD** – LET'S HEAR IT, CLYDE!

I WANTED YEW TO COME **UNDERGROUND** YEW WANTED ME TO COME OUT THERE-ERE-

YEW SAID OUR CHI-ILD NEEDED NATURE'S GREENERY- SUN AND SCENERY I SAID KIDS ARE KIDS ANY WHERE-ERE

YEW SAID GOODBYE
AND I DUG A HOLE
UNDER GROUND
YEW MARCHED
AWAY
WITH A PICKET SI-IGN

BUT WHEREVER YOU GO
I'LL WAIT IN MY HOVEL
'TILL THAT GOLDEN DAY
WHEN YEW'LL APPEAR
WITH A SHOVEL
IN OUR FALL OUT LOVE NEST
UNDER GROUND!

WHEN FIRST
I DANCED
IT WAS
MY MEANS
OF COMMUNI-
CATING
WITH THE
WORLD.

WHEN I DID **THIS** AND **THIS**
I WAS SAYING TO THE
WORLD THAT MAN MUST
LIVE IN HAPPINESS AND
PEACE AND
MUTUAL LOVE.

BUT THE
WORLD
MISINTER-
PRETED
AND
SAID I
WAS
OBSCURE.

I GREW
BITTER
TOWARD
THE
WORLD.
WHEN
NEXT I
DANCED
IT WAS FOR
NEUROTIC
SELF-
EXPRESSION

WHEN I DID **THIS**
AND **THIS**
I WAS TELLING THE
WORLD THAT IT
COULD GO ITS WAY
AND I WOULD GO
MINE.

BUT THE
WORLD
MISINTERPRETED
AND SAID
I WAS
OBSCENE.

NOW I'VE WITHDRAWN BEYOND THE NEED FOR COMMUNICATION.

WHEN I NOW DO **THIS** AND **THIS** IT'S OUT OF SHEER BOREDOM.

CHA CHA CHA

THE WORLD
THINKS
I'M A
THRILL
CRAZY
KID.

EVER SINCE THEY WERE
LITTLE I TOLD THEM—
THEY'D GROW UP, THEY'D
LEAVE US, THEY'D BREAK
OUR HEARTS. DID I OR
DIDN'T I TELL THEM?

— THAT'S THE
WAY CHIL-
DREN ARE
TODAY. THEY
DON'T
LISTEN.

AND WHAT DID THEY
SAY? "NO, PA! NO!
WE'LL **ALWAYS**
LOOK AFTER YOU!"
DID THEY OR
DIDN'T THEY?

— CHILDREN
ALWAYS
HAVE TO
CONTRADICT

SO ONE DAY IT'S "WE'LL NEVER LEAVE YOU" AND THE **NEXT** DAY IT'S "DON'T I HAVE THE RIGHT TO A LITTLE PRIVACY?"

PRIVACY! WHO PAID THEIR DOCTOR BILLS?

SO THEY GREW UP. AND THEY **LEFT** US. SO WHO WAS RIGHT? THE FATHER OR THE CHILDREN?

A CHILD RIGHT? **HOW** COULD A CHILD BE RIGHT?

BUT A **FUNNY** THING
HAPPENED. THEY DIDN'T
BREAK MY HEART. AS A
MATTER OF FACT I
FELT A **WHOLE LOT**
BETTER.

ME TOO.
ONE
HUNDRED
PER CENT!

AFTER ALL THESE
YEARS WHAT A
DISCOVERY TO
MAKE —

WE NEVER
LIKED
CHILDREN.

DEAR MOTHER—
ARRIVED IN CAMP THIS A.M.
RECEIVED SIX SHOTS AND AN
INDOCTRINATION LECTURE
ABOUT DEFENDING THE FREE
WORLD. I
WANT TO
COME HOME—

DEAR SON—
BE A MAN. YOU ARE
ALWAYS WITH US IN
OUR HEARTS. WE ARE
SURE YOU'LL GET
USED TO IT—

DEAR MOTHER-
THIS A.M. THEY SHOWED US FILMS
ABOUT THE ENEMIES OF THE FREE
WORLD. THEY ARE ALL FROM THE
UNIVERSITY OF CALIFORNIA. ONE
OF THE FELLOWS IN OUR
BARRACKS COMES
FROM THERE. WE
ARE HIDING HIM.
I WANT TO
COME HOME-

DEAR SON-
TELL YOUR SERGEANT WE'D
ONLY SEND YOU TO A <u>GOOD</u>
SCHOOL. BE A MAN. DON'T
ASSOCIATE WITH
TROUBLEMAKERS.
YOU ARE ALWAYS
WITH US IN OUR
HEARTS-

DEAR MOTHER —
MARCHED TO AND FROM THE CHURCH
OF OUR CHOICE THIS A.M. AND GIVEN
OUR 12TH INDOCTRINATION LECTURE.
CAPTAIN TOLD US WE IN THE FREE
WORLD MUST DEFEND
OURSELVES AGAINST
ENEMIES FROM WITHIN.
EVERYONE WHO
CHOSE WRONG
CHURCH OF HIS
CHOICE RECEIVED A
STERN WARNING. I
WANT TO COME HOME —

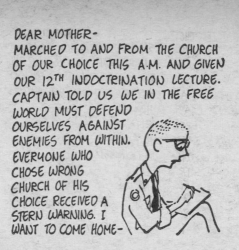

DEAR SON —
I'M SURE YOUR CAPTAIN IS
ONLY INTERESTED IN WHAT'S
BEST FOR YOU AND, AS DO
WE, HAS YOU ALWAYS WITH
HIM IN HIS HEART.
ASK HIM TO
CHECK OFF
THE RIGHT
CHURCH FOR
US TO GO TO.
BE A MAN.

DEAR MOTHER—
RECEIVED OUR 25TH INDOCTRINATION LECTURE
THIS A.M. FROM A _NEW_ CAPTAIN. HE SAID THE
ARMY WAS LIBERALIZING ITS INFORMATION
PROGRAM AND ENCOURAGED US TO ASK QUES-
TIONS. I ASKED HIM TO
DEFINE "FREE WORLD". THE
CAPTAIN CALLED ME A PINKO
COLLEGE WISE GUY, ORDERED
ME ON EXTRA DETAIL,
AND WANTED TO KNOW
WHAT KIND OF FAMILY
I CAME FROM. I WANT
TO COME HOME —

DEAR SON—
IF YOU CAME HOME NOW THEY'D ONLY
FOLLOW YOU TO FIND US. DON'T TELL
THEM A THING UNTIL WE'RE ABLE
TO MOVE AND CHANGE OUR NAME.
PLEASE FOR OUR SAKE
STOP MAKING TROUBLE
AND BE A MAN!
WHEREVER WE GO
YOU AND YOUR ARMY
WILL ALWAYS BE
WITH US IN OUR
HEARTS.

SO I WAS WATCHING
SAM BENEDICT
AND EVERYBODY
WAS ATTACKING
HIM BECAUSE
IN COURT HE
WAS DEFENDING
A NAZI AND
A COMMUNIST.

THE RAT!

WELL, NOT EXACTLY. DID YOU KNOW THAT IN THIS COUNTRY THE SUPREME COURT HAS SAID THAT ITS NOT ACTUALLY AGAINST THE **LAW** TO NOT HAVE A RELIGION!

COME ON!

THEN ON **NAKED CITY** A COUPLE OF DAYS LATER THEY HAD THIS CASE WHERE THE POLICE TAPPED THESE TELEPHONE CALLS BUT THE CASE GOT THROWN OUT OF COURT!

YOU MEAN WIRE TAPPING IS **ILLEGAL?**

IT IS TIME FOR
A SERIOUS
CRITICAL
EVALUATION
OF THIS
SEASON'S
TV NEWS
PROGRAMS.
NUMBER ONE—
THE HUNTLEY,
BRINKLEY
SHOW.

IT IS NOT THE NEWS THAT IS IMPORTANT
IN THIS PROGRAM. RATHER, IT IS THE
COMPLEX RELATIONSHIP OF THE TWO
HEROES. THE VIEWER IS COMPELLED
TO ASK. DO THEY LIKE EACH
OTHER TODAY? WOULD DAVID
PREFER TO WORK IN NEW
YORK? WOULD CHET PREFER
WASHINGTON? WHEN CHET SEEMS
DEPRESSED BY EVENTS WE WORRY,
NOT BECAUSE OF THE EVENT, BUT
BECAUSE OF ITS EFFECT ON CHET.

WHILE HUNTLEY AND BRINKLEY MAKE THE NEWS LESS IMPORTANT BECAUSE OF THEIR PERSONAL INVOLVEMENT WITH IT, CRONKITE MAKES THE NEWS MORE IMPORTANT BECAUSE HE DEIGNS TO ASSOCIATE WITH IT.

CRONKITE IS OUR HERO. THE NEWS AROUND HIM IS A SOCIAL CLIMBER. THEREFORE VIET NAM IS IMPORTANT WHEN CRONKITE SAYS SO, **NOT** WHEN VIET NAM SAYS SO. CRONKITE KNOWS. **TRUST** CRONKITE.

WHILE EACH OF THESE SHOWS HAS ITS OBVIOUS MERITS, ONE CAN NOT HELP BUT FEEL THAT A MERGER WOULD IMPROVE THE QUALITY OF BOTH. CRONKITE, PERHAPS, PLAYING THE FATHER ROLE, HUNTLEY AND BRINKLEY HIS SOMBRE AND WITTY SONS. EACH OBSERVING WORLD AFFAIRS BY HIS OWN LIGHT AND GAINING A DEEPER KNOWLEGE OF HIS PLACE IN THAT WORLD AS THE TELEVISION SEASON PROGRESSES.

WHEN DAVID BECOMES INCREASINGLY WRY WE WANT TO SHAKE HIM "DAVID, DAVID," WE WOULD LIKE TO CRY OUT, "DO YOU NOT SEE HOW SAD CHET IS? HELP HIM, FOR HEAVENS SAKE! HELP HIM!" AND WHEN EITHER CHET OR DAVID IS AWAY ON HOLIDAY WE BECOME BORED. OF WHAT IMPORTANCE ARE WORLD AFFAIRS ONCE THE HUMAN INTEREST IS REMOVED?

SECOND, LET US LOOK AT THE WALTER CRONKITE SHOW. UNLIKE CHET AND DAVID, CRONKITE DOES NOT USE THE NEWS AS A BACKGROUND. CRONKITE IS THE NEWS. WE ONLY NEED LOOK AT HIM TO KNOW THAT IT WAS HE WHO SENT UP GLENN, SCHIRRA AND CARPENTER - AND IT WAS HE WHO BROUGHT THEM DOWN SAFELY.

UNTIL ONE DAY- A TALL
DARK STRANGER RIDES
INTO TOWN - IT IS
JOHN DALY.

OUR SUBJECT TODAY IS
URBAN ARCHITECTURE
OF THE NINETEENTH
AND TWENTIETH
CENTURIES—BASED ON
EXCAVATION AND
RECONSTRUCTION OF
THE RUINS OF THAT
PERIOD IN HISTORY.

OF COURSE, WITH THE EVIDENCE
OF SO MUCH TOTAL DESTRUC-
TION WE ASSUMED THE
RUINS WERE CREATED BY
WAR- UNTIL A CHANCE
DISCOVERY OF A HIDDEN
DOCUMENT PROVED THAT
IT WASN'T WAR AT ALL-
IT WAS A **GUERILLA**
INSURRECTION—SOMETHING
CALLED "URBAN RENEWAL"

OUR FIRST SLIDE SHOWS A
RECONSTRUCTION OF THE
EARLIEST AND MOST **PRIMITIVE**
FORM OF THAT PERIOD— THE
GLASS SLAB- BUILT
PROBABLY IN THE MIDDLE
NINETEENTH CENTURY-
NOTICE ITS **VACUOUSNESS**
AND LACK OF SCALE.

NEXT WE HAVE A **LATER** MORE **TRANSITIONAL** HOUSE OF THE EARLY TWENTIETH CENTURY- **STILL** RATHER MONOTONOUS BUT FEATURING GREATER SOPHISTICATION OF **DETAIL**. THE RECORDS WE FOUND PROVE THAT THESE CONSTRUCTIONS WERE AT FIRST KNOWN AS "**HOUSING PROJECTS**" A CLUMSY TERM LATER SIMPLIFIED INTO "SLUMS."

OUR **LAST** SLIDE REPRESENTS A **HIGH** POINT OF PROGRESS. BUILT IN THE LATE TWENTIETH OR EARLY TWENTY-FIRST CENTURY THIS BUILDING KNOWN AS A "BROWNSTONE" UTILIZES A TASTE AND A FLAIR FOR EXPERIMENTATION THAT SUGGEST AN ARCHITECTURAL RENAISSANCE.

ONE CAN ONLY BE LEFT BREATHLESS BY THE BRILLIANCE OF A SOCIETY THAT WAS ABLE TO MAKE SUCH GIANT STRIDES IN A MERE ONE-HUNDRED FIFTY YEARS.

SOMETIMES I WANT SO HARD FOR A RELATIONSHIP TO BE MEANINGFUL THAT I READ MEANINGFUL THINGS INTO IT—

— AND THEY'RE NOT **THERE!** THAT'S **FALSE MEANINGFULNESS!** I DO THAT **ALWAYS!**

AND THEN I GET BITTER AND **BLAME** PEOPLE WHEN **ACTUALLY** IT'S NOT **ANYBODY'S** FAULT..

A MEANINGFUL RELATION-SHIP CAN **NOT** BE BUILT ON BLAME. IF IT TURNS OUT TO BE JUST MAKING OUT I GUESS ALL ONE CAN DO IS **ACCEPT** IT.

I'D HATE FOR IT TO BE MAKING OUT WITH **US**, BERNARD

I COULDN'T STAND IT, DOROTHY. BUT **WHAT** CAN WE DO? WE CAN'T RUN **AWAY.**

MY DREAM HAS ALWAYS
BEEN TO WRITE A NOVEL
ON THE CULTURAL
BREAKDOWN OF THE
MIDDLE CLASS.

BUT I'VE LONG FELT AN
INABILITY TO COMMUNICATE.
WHEN ALL IS SAID AND
DONE - DO I **REALLY**
KNOW PEOPLE?

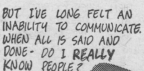

SO I TOOK LEAVE OF THE
UNIVERSITY AND ASSUMED AN
OFFICE POSITION FEELING
THAT THE PRESSURE OF
DAILY CONTACT WOULD LEND
ME INSIGHTS INTO THE
ORIENTATION,
HABITS AND
GROUP
NEEDS
OF MY
FELLOW
WORKERS

BUT I COULDN'T COMMUNICATE
WITH THEM. WHEN I TRIED
TO LEAD DISCUSSIONS ON
THE CULTURAL BREAKDOWN
OF THE MIDDLE CLASS
ALL **THEY'D** TALK ABOUT
WAS **BASEBALL**.

SO I PUT ASIDE THE NOTES FOR
MY NOVEL AND BONED UP ON THE
SPORTS PAGE FINDING THAT, IN
TIME, I WAS READY TO SUBTLY
LEAD OFFICE CONVERSATION FROM
BASEBALL AS A SPORT TO BASEBALL
AS A FACTOR IN THE CULTURAL
BREAKDOWN OF
THE MIDDLE
CLASS.

BUT AT THAT POINT THE **FOOTBALL**
SEASON BEGAN. SO IN ORDER TO RE-
ESTABLISH RAPPORT I HAD TO ABAN-
DON THE NOTES FOR MY NOVEL AND
BONE UP ON THE SPORTS PAGE TILL
I FOUND MYSELF READY TO SUBTLY
MANIPULATE OFFICE DISCUSSION INTO
THE INTER-RELATION-
SHIP BETWEEN
BASEBALL,
FOOTBALL
AND THE
CULTURAL
BREAK-
DOWN OF
THE
MIDDLE
CLASS.

WHICH IS WHEN
THE BASKETBALL
SEASON BEGAN.

AND SOON
AFTER —
ICE HOCKEY.

I'VE FINALLY HAD TO ABANDON
MY NOVEL. IN ANY EVENT IT'S
ALL BEGUN TO SEEM A BIT
SUPERFICIAL. BESIDES I'M
MUCH TOO BUSY KEEPING UP
WITH THE
SPORTS
PAGE.

HOWEVER I **AM**
COMMUNICATING
EXTREMELY WELL.

EVER SINCE I WAS
A LITTLE KID I
DIDN'T WANT TO BE
ME. I WANTED TO
BE BILLIE WIDDLEDON.
AND BILLIE WIDDLEDON
DIDN'T EVEN **LIKE** ME.

I WALKED LIKE **HE**
WALKED. I TALKED
LIKE **HE** TALKED. I
SIGNED UP FOR THE
HIGH SCHOOL **HE**
SIGNED UP FOR-

WHICH WAS WHEN BILLIE
WIDDLEDON CHANGED. HE
BEGAN TO HANG AROUND
HERBY VANDEMAN. HE
WALKED LIKE HERBY
VANDEMAN. HE **TALKED**
LIKE HERBY VANDEMAN.

HE MIXED ME UP! I
BEGAN TO WALK AND
TALK LIKE BILLIE
WIDDLEDON WALKING
AND TALKING LIKE
HERBY VANDEMAN.

AND THEN IT DAWNED
ON ME THAT HERBY
VANDEMAN WALKED
AND TALKED LIKE
JOEY HAVERLIN AND
JOEY HAVERLIN
WALKED AND
TALKED LIKE
CORKY
SABINSON.

SO HERE I AM WALKING
AND TALKING LIKE
BILLIE WIDDLEDON'S
IMITATION OF HERBY
VANDEMAN'S VERSION
OF JOEY HAVERLIN
TRYING TO WALK
AND TALK LIKE
CORKY SABINSON.

AND **WHO** DO YOU THINK CORKY SABINSON IS ALWAYS WALKING AND TALKING LIKE? OF **ALL** PEOPLE— DOPEY KENNY WELLINGTON—

THAT LITTLE PEST WHO WALKS AND TALKS LIKE ME.

YOUR FATHER DIDN'T GET A **BANK** LOAN TO BUILD **YOU** A **LIBRARY**, MISTER! YOU DO YOUR READING SOMEWHERE **ELSE** THAN HIS FALLOUT SHELTER!

IT'S **MY** FALLOUT SHELTER **TOO**, MA!

ARGUMENTS! ARGUMENTS! YOU SAY IT'S **YOURS** — YOUR **SISTER** SAYS IT'S **HERS** — IT'S **EVERYBODY'S** FALLOUT SHELTER BUT **MAMA'S**!

YOU NEVER YELL AT SISTER WHEN **SHE'S** IN HERE.

FOR YEARS THOSE OF US WHO
HAVE TOILED IN THE VINEYARDS
OF SUBURBAN CIVIL DEFENSE
HAVE BEEN CONCERNED WITH
THE PROBLEM OF HOW TO
MAINTAIN LAW AND ORDER
FOLLOWING A NUCLEAR ASSAULT.

THE BIG CITIES WOULD, OF COURSE,
BE ANNIHILATED, THEREBY
SIMPLIFYING **THEIR** CIVIL
DEFENSE PROBLEMS
IMMEASURABLY. HOWEVER,
FOR THOSE OF US IN **SUBURBIA**
THERE ARE **BOUND** TO BE
COMPLICATIONS.

WE WOULD BE SUBJECT TO
MASS ONSLAUGHTS OF
REFUGEES FROM THE CITY.
WHILE OUR HEARTS, AS
ALL HEARTS MUST, GO OUT
TO THESE VICTIMS THEY
DO POSE A THREAT TO
OUR CAREFULLY PLANNED
PROGRAM.

HOW CAN ONE TELL A RADIO-ACTIVE MOB THAT THEY WOULDN'T BE HAPPY IN OUR TOWN? NO, WE CAN ONLY PRESERVE OUR WAY OF LIFE BY BARRICADING OUR STREETS AND RE-DIRECTING ALL MIGRANT TRAFFIC TO THE PUBLIC HIGH-WAYS, AIDING THEM PERHAPS, WITH IMPROVED DIRECTIONAL SIGNS AND FREE ROAD MAPS.

BUT WHEN MAN'S SURVIVAL IS AT STAKE HE MAY WELL SURRENDER TO THE **BASER** INSTINCTS. OUR BARRICADES MIGHT HAVE TO BE DEFENDED BY **FORCE OF ARMS**. BUT JUST AS WE ARE WILLING TO GO TO WAR TO DEFEND OUR FREEDOM SO WE SHALL BE WILLING TO DEFEND WHAT'S LEFT OF IT BY MANNING THE SUBURBAN BARRICADES !

IN SUBURBAN CIVIL
DEFENSE OUR MOTTO IS:
IF YOU CAN'T GET
YOURSELF A RUSSIAN,
SETTLE FOR AN
AMERICAN.

"LOOK AT HIM," THEY
USED TO SAY.
"PRESIDENT OF THE
COMPANY,"
THEY USED
TO SAY.

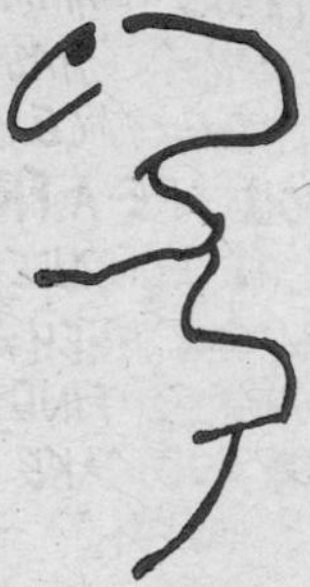

AND I USED TO SMILE
AND BUY MORE
STOCK AND MOVE
EVEN **HIGHER**.
"LOOK AT HIM,"
THEY USED TO
SAY.

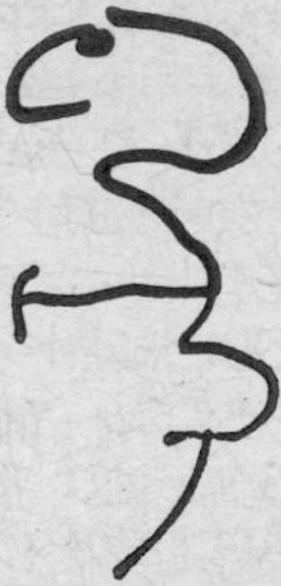

AND ALL THE TIME—WHILE **THEY**
WERE LOOKING AND **I** WAS SMILING—
INSIDE ME A LITTLE VOICE WAS
TALKING—YAMMER,
YAMMER, YAMMER—
A LITTLE VOICE SAYING—
"YOU ARE A **FRAUD**,
IRWIN CORPULENT.
SOMEDAY THEY'RE
GOING TO FIND YOU
OUT AND TAKE IT
ALL AWAY."

I REASONED WITH THE LITTLE VOICE
BUT IT DIDN'T DO ANY GOOD. "I'M
HONEST!" I ARGUED. "I **DESERVE**
TO BE WHERE I AM!"
BUT THE LITTLE VOICE
JUST REPEATED—
"SOMEDAY THEY'RE
GOING TO FIND YOU
OUT, IRWIN CORPULENT.
SOMEDAY THEY'RE
GOING TO TAKE IT
ALL AWAY."

I **IGNORED** THE VOICE. I INVESTED **MORE**. I MADE A **LOT** OF MONEY. BUT THE **HIGHER** I WENT THE **SHAKIER** I FELT. THEN ONE DAY A COMMITTEE OF TOTAL STRANGERS CAME INTO MY OFFICE. "WHAT CAN I DO FOR YOU?" I ASKED, THINKING IT MIGHT BE ANOTHER GOOD CITIZENSHIP AWARD.

"YOU ARE A FRAUD, IRWIN CORPULENT," THEY SAID TO ME. "WE HAVE FOUND YOU OUT AND WE ARE TAKING IT ALL AWAY."

I CLEANED OUT
MY DESK AND
I LEFT.

WHEN THEY FIND
YOU OUT THEY
FIND YOU OUT.
WHY ARGUE.

BUT ITS MY POLICY TO CULTIVATE THOSE THINGS IN LIFE THAT I FEAR THE MOST. I FEEL IF YOU'RE **AFRAID** OF SOMETHING ITS ALWAYS BEST TO NEGOTIATE.

FOR INSTANCE, IF I PET YOU WOULD **THAT** MAKE US FRIENDS? **MAY I** PET YOU? WOULD YOU **SNARL** AT ME IF I PET YOU?

I MADE GREAT FRIENDS WITH
A VERY HOSTILE CAT THIS
MORNING. IS IT ALL RIGHT
IF I PET YOU?

LAST WEEK I GOT A PARAKEET
TO SIT ON MY FINGER.
PARAKEETS, I'M TOLD, CAN TAKE
THE TRUE MEASURE OF A PERSON.
WILL YOU BITE
IF I PET YOU?

I'M GOING TO PET YOU **NOW**, DOGGIE.
YOU'LL SEE IT WILL BE ALL RIGHT
AND WE'LL BECOME **DEAR** AND
DEVOTED FRIENDS. I'M GOING TO PET
YOU **RIGHT** NOW. **THERE!** I PET YOU!

EVEN WHEN I'M ABLE TO
GIVE I FEEL I'M ONLY
BEING TOLERATED.

TRY TO SEE IT MY WAY. I AM NEARLY TWENTY AND IF I WAS **EVER** GOING TO MAKE THE BREAK **NOW** WAS THE TIME TO DO IT. IMAGINE, HALF MY GIRL FRIENDS WERE ALREADY SEPARATED FROM THEIR HUSBANDS AND HERE I WAS STILL LIVING AT **HOME!**

SO I TOLD MY PARENTS I WAS MOVING OUT.

YOU CAN'T IMAGINE THE YELLING
AND SCREAMING. MY FATHER SAID-
"YOU'RE BREAKING YOUR MOTHER'S
HEART!" MY MOTHER SAID-
"WHAT WAS MY CRIME? WHAT
WAS MY TERRIBLE CRIME?"

AND BEFORE I KNEW IT WE WERE IN
THE MIDDLE OF A BIG ARGUMENT
AND I TOLD THEM THEY BOTH
NEEDED ANALYSIS AND THEY
TOLD ME I HAD A FILTHY MOUTH
AND SUDDENLY I WAS OUT ON
THE STREET WITH MY RAINCOAT,
MY SUITCASE AND MY TENNIS
RACKET BUT I HAD NO PLACE
TO MOVE!

SO I LOOKED AROUND DOWNTOWN
AND EVERYTHING WAS TOO EXPEN-
SIVE AND EVENING CAME AND
ALL MY GIRL FRIENDS HAD
RECONCILED WITH THEIR HUSBANDS
SO THERE WAS ABSOLUTELY NO
PLACE I COULD SPEND THE NIGHT.

WELL, **FRANKLY**, WHAT ON EARTH
COULD I **DO**? I WAITED TILL IT
WAS **WAY** PAST MY PARENTS BED-
TIME - THEN I **SNEAKED** BACK
INTO THE HOUSE AND SET THE
ALARM IN MY BEDROOM FOR
SIX THE NEXT MORNING.

THEN I SLEPT ON TOP OF THE
BED SO I WOULDN'T WRINKLE
ANY SHEETS. SNEAKED SOME
BREAKFAST IN THE MORNING
AND GOT OUT BEFORE ANY-
ONE WAS UP.

I'VE BEEN
LIVING THAT
WAY FOR
TWO MONTHS
NOW.

EVERY NIGHT AFTER MIDNIGHT
I SNEAK INTO MY BEDROOM,
SLEEP ON TOP OF THE BED
TILL SIX THE NEXT MORNING,
HAVE BREAKFAST AND SNEAK
OUT.

AND EVERY DAY I CALL UP MY
PARENTS FROM THE DOWNSTAIRS
DRUGSTORE AND THEY YELL
AND CRY AT ME TO COME
BACK. BUT, OF COURSE, I
ALWAYS TELL THEM NO.

PEACE MARCHERS IN A **COMIC STRIP**? YOU **CAN'T** BE SERIOUS!

YES SIR! **THERE THEY** ARE MARCHING ON THIS MISSILE BASE THAT COLONEL CANYON IS IN COMMAND OF.

COLONEL CANYON? YOU MEAN **STEVE** CANYON? I THOUGHT HE WAS ONLY A **CAPTAIN!**

CAPTAINS HARDLY MAKE IT IN COMIC STRIPS ANYMORE. YOU REMEMBER HOW THEY USED TO DATE MAGAZINES MONTHS AHEAD SO YOU'D THINK THEY WERE **BETTER**? WELL, THAT'S HOW THEY RANK OFFICERS IN COMIC STRIPS. TERRY LEE MUST AT LEAST BE A **MAJOR** BY NOW. AND BUZ SAWYER-WELL, I'M AFRAID TO GUESS!

BUT STEVE CAN-
YON OUTRANKS
THEM ALL. RIGHT?
NOBODY OUTRANKS
STEVE CANYON -
EXCEPT MAYBE
PAT RYAN.

I DON'T KNOW HOW IT WORKS.
TIME IN GRADE OR SOMETHING.
ANYHOW STEVE CANYON ISN'T A
BLACK AND WHITE COLD WARRIOR
LIKE THE OTHER COMIC STRIPS!
HE TELLS THE PEACE MARCHERS
THEY CAN PICKET
ALL THEY WANT
BECAUSE THAT'S
THEIR RIGHT
AS AMERICANS.

BUZ
SAWYER
WOULD
NEVER
DO
THAT

ALL HE ASKS THEM TO DO
IS PROVE THEIR CITIZEN-
SHIP: SHOW THEIR PASSPORTS
OR THEIR FIRST PAPERS
OR SOMETHING.

I USED TO READ THEM ADS – KNOW WHAT I MEAN? "EVEN YOUR BEST FRIEND WON'T TELL YOU" ADS – AND IT USED TO BOTHER ME BECAUSE IF YOU'RE A **RIGHT** GUY – NICE TO YOUR MOTHER AND EVERYTHING – WHAT KIND OF GIRL IS IT WHO'D GIVE YOU THE GATE BECAUSE OF THE **WRONG** TOOTHPASTE YOU USE – OR WHAT KIND OF PHONEY FRIEND IS IT WHO'D SPEND HIS TIME NOT DRINKING WITH YOU BUT **SMELLING** YOU?

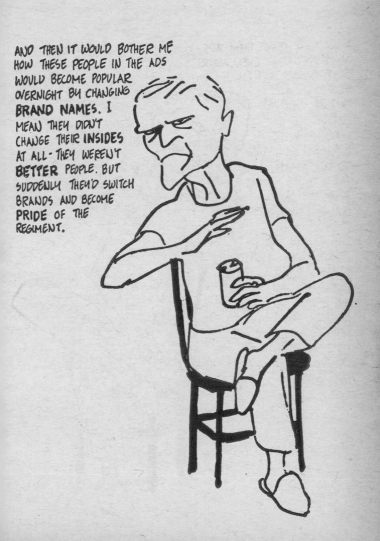

AND THEN IT WOULD BOTHER ME HOW THESE PEOPLE IN THE ADS WOULD BECOME POPULAR OVERNIGHT BY CHANGING **BRAND NAMES.** I MEAN THEY DIDN'T CHANGE THEIR **INSIDES** AT ALL - THEY WEREN'T **BETTER** PEOPLE. BUT SUDDENLY THEY'D SWITCH BRANDS AND BECOME **PRIDE** OF THE REGIMENT.

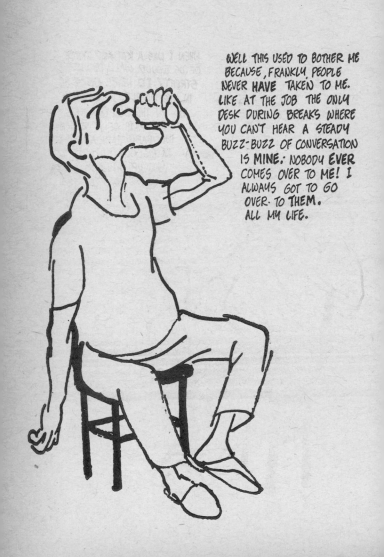

WELL THIS USED TO BOTHER ME
BECAUSE, FRANKLY, PEOPLE
NEVER **HAVE** TAKEN TO ME.
LIKE AT THE JOB THE ONLY
DESK DURING BREAKS WHERE
YOU CAN'T HEAR A STEADY
BUZZ-BUZZ OF CONVERSATION
IS **MINE.** NOBODY **EVER**
COMES OVER TO ME! I
ALWAYS GOT TO GO
OVER TO **THEM.**
ALL MY LIFE.

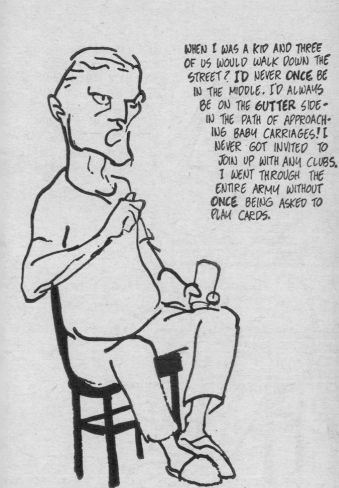

WHEN I WAS A KID AND THREE OF US WOULD WALK DOWN THE STREET? I'D NEVER **ONCE** BE IN THE MIDDLE. I'D ALWAYS BE ON THE **GUTTER** SIDE—IN THE PATH OF APPROACHING BABY CARRIAGES! I NEVER GOT INVITED TO JOIN UP WITH ANY CLUBS. I WENT THROUGH THE ENTIRE ARMY WITHOUT **ONCE** BEING ASKED TO PLAY CARDS.

AND I ADMIT SOMETIMES I USED TO WAKE UP IN THE MIDDLE OF THE NIGHT DRIPPING SWEAT. AND GOING ON AND OFF IN MY HEAD LIKE A BIG NEON SIGN WAS: "BAD BREATH, BAD BREATH, BAD BREATH."

I GOT MARRIED AND MY WIFE TREATED ME LIKE A JANITOR. THE ONLY THING SHE COULD SAY NICE FOR ME WAS THAT I'M GOOD WITH MY HANDS. WHEN THE OTHER WIVES BOASTED ABOUT **THEIR** HUSBANDS TALENTS SHE'D CALL ME IN TO PUT UP A SHELF. SO AT PARTIES I'D DO MY FAMOUS "PUTTING UP THE SHELF BIT" AND THE REST OF THE TIME WE WERE **STRANGERS.**

AND MORE AND MORE IN THE BACK OF MY HEAD IT WENT- "CHANGE YOUR SOAP. CHANGE YOUR TOOTHPASTE" BUT - I DON'T KNOW - I ALWAYS FELT THAT I'M ME FOR BETTER OR WORSE. I'M ME!

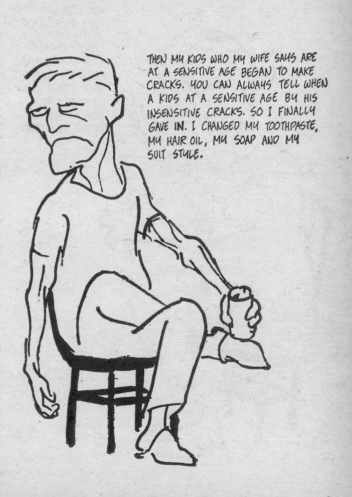

THEN MY KIDS WHO MY WIFE SAYS ARE
AT A SENSITIVE AGE BEGAN TO MAKE
CRACKS. YOU CAN ALWAYS TELL WHEN
A KIDS AT A SENSITIVE AGE BY HIS
INSENSITIVE CRACKS. SO I FINALLY
GAVE IN. I CHANGED MY TOOTHPASTE,
MY HAIR OIL, MY SOAP AND MY
SUIT STYLE.

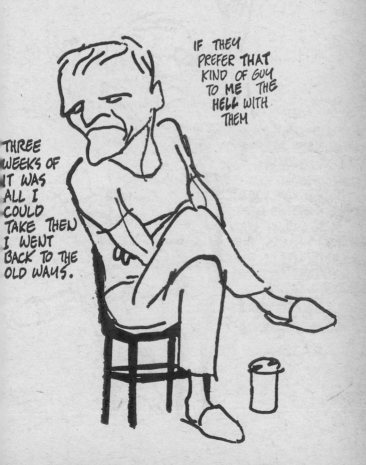

IF THEY
PREFER THAT
KIND OF GUY
TO ME THE
HELL WITH
THEM

THREE
WEEKS OF
IT WAS
ALL I
COULD
TAKE THEN
I WENT
BACK TO THE
OLD WAYS.

WE HAVE FORGOTTEN
THAT THE BEST
TRAINING A PURELY
CINEMATIC ACTOR
CAN HAVE IS
SWIMMING –

HE LEARNS
GRAPHIC RHYTHM.
HE LEARNS
BALANCED
FLUIDITY. HE
LEARNS
PHYSICAL
PROJECTION.

BRANDO IN A WAY KNOWS
THIS. I SUSPECT THAT
SECRETLY HE SWIMS.
ELSE HOW COULD HE
COME CLOSEST
TO THAT
GREATEST OF
HERO-VIRILITY-
GODS THE
CINEMA HAS
YET PRODUCED—

—JOHNNY
WEISSMULLER.

STUDY THE ECONOMY
OF LANGUAGE IN THE
EARLY WEISSMULLER
CYCLE. THE **CLEAN,
UNCLUTTERED**
PLOT STRUCTURE—
THE **DARKS**
OF HIDDEN
PASSION—

—BETWEEN MAN
AND ALLIGATOR,
BETWEEN MAN
AND APE, BETWEEN
MAN AND ELEPHANT.
DOES NOT SOME
OF THIS ANTICI-
PATE TENNES-
SEE WILLIAMS?

THE NEO-BERGMANESQUE
RELIGIOUS THEME - THE
ALWAYS ALIENATED
TARZAN - UNABLE
TO TRULY
COMMUNICATE
IN A JUNGLE
NOT OF
HIS OWN
MAKING.

IN ANOTHER
SOCIETY MIGHT
HE NOT HAVE
BEEN
BYRON?

AND WHO BETTER THAN
WEISSMULLER CAN
PORTRAY THIS?
IMPASSIVE YET TENDER.
SWINGING THROUGH
TREES (HOW
CONSCIOUSLY
FREUDIAN)
WITH THE
CONTROLLED
ARTISTRY OF
THE TRUE MIME.

HAS THE
PLASTICITY
OF CINEMA
EVER BEEN
SHOWN TO
BETTER
EFFECT?

WITH THE DECLINE OF WEISSMULLER, FOLLOWED BY THE RETIREMENT OF BUSTER CRABBE FROM THE FLASH GORDON SERIALS, BASIC CINEMA RECEIVED A BLOW FROM WHICH IT IS ONLY NOW BEGINNING TO RECOVER.

WE'VE ALL HEARD OF THE RADICAL RIGHT AND THE RADICAL LEFT. WITH US TONIGHT IS A SPOKESMAN OF A GROUP WHOSE VIEWS WE'VE HEARD VERY LITTLE ABOUT: THE RADICAL MIDDLE.

GOOD MORNING. GOOD AFTERNOON. GOOD EVENING.

WOULD YOU DESCRIBE THE VIEWS OF YOUR ORGANIZATION, SIR?

PROBABLY. THE RADICAL MIDDLE THINKS IT'S TIME WE TOOK THE INITIATIVE IN WORLD AFFAIRS, WHILE DEPLORING THE IDEA OF CHANGE FOR MERE CHANGE'S SAKE.

WE OPPOSE CONCESSIONS TO THE SOVIETS. HOWEVER, WE FAVOR NEGOTIATIONS AND STRONGLY SUPPORT THE U.N., WHILE WE REJECT ITS INTERFERENCE WITH OUR BASIC INTERESTS.

WE FAVOR ARMS CONTROL AND A
CONTINUED BUILDUP, A STRONG
CIVIL RIGHTS PROGRAM WITHOUT
THE UNDUE HASTE WHICH CREATES
DEEP SCARS. \

THEN, SIR,
SUMMING UP
WISE, YOU'D
SAY YOUR
PHILOSOPHY
IS — ? —

BOLD TIMES CALL FOR BOLD
ANSWERS. WITHIN REASON.
IN A MANNER OF SPEAKING.
MORE OR LESS.

_THANK YOU,
SIR.

ON THE
OTHER
HAND—

ONCE THERE WAS A SLEEPING COUNTRY THAT HAD SPENT EIGHT YEARS UNDER A SPELL. NOBODY TALKED. NOBODY ARGUED. EVERYBODY SLEPT.

THEN ONE DAY INTO THIS COUNTRY RODE A HANDSOME YOUNG PRINCE. "IT'S TIME TO GET MOVING AGAIN," THE PRINCE DECLARED. THE COUNTRY STIRRED IN ITS SLEEP.

FOR THE FIRST TIME IN YEARS PEOPLE ACTUALLY BEGAN TO TALK. THEY **ARGUED**. THEY **TOOK SIDES**. "STOP TALKING SO LOUD!" THE REST OF THE COUNTRY GRUMBLED IN ITS SLEEP. "HAVE SOME CONSIDERATION FOR THE REST OF US."

BUT THE TALKING ONLY BECAME LOUDER. MORE AND MORE PEOPLE AWOKE AND, ANGRY THAT THEY HAD TO BE AWAKE, BEGAN TO **TALK**, BEGAN TO **ARGUE**, BEGAN TO **TAKE SIDES.**

THEN ONE DAY THE YOUNG PRINCE WAS KILLED— NO ONE COULD AGREE BY WHOM. EVERY SIDE ACCUSED EVERY OTHER SIDE. BUT CALMER HEADS PREVAILED.

"SEE WHAT WE HAVE COME TO WITH THIS WICKED DISSEN- SION" CALMER HEADS ARGUED, "LET US CLEANSE OUR SOCIETY OF THIS DIVISIVE DEBATE!"

AND THE COUNTRY, SUFFERING FROM WOUNDS AND GUILT, **CHEERED.** DEBATE HALTED. ARGUMENT DIED. AND THERE WAS NO MORE TALK IN THE LAND.

AND AS THE COUNTRY PREPARED FOR SLEEP IT HOPED NO ONE WOULD EVER ASK IT TO MOVE AGAIN—

FOR IT
REALLY
DID NOT
WANT TO
KILL ANY-
MORE
PRINCES.

A DANCE
TO THE
NEW YEAR.

IN THIS DANCE
I HAVE
SYMBOLIZED
PEACE ON
EARTH AND
GOOD WILL
TO ALL MEN.

UM- I DON'T WANT YOU
TO THINK I MEAN
ANYTHING **FUNNY**
BY THAT STATEMENT-
I MEAN PEACE, YES-
BUT WITHOUT APPEASE-
MENT ON THE
AFOREMENTIONED
EARTH AND, NATURALLY,
GOOD WILL TO
ALL MEN.

UH-WAIT A MINUTE-BY
GOOD WILL I MEAN
THAT WE SHOULD
HAVE GOOD WILL TO
THOSE WHO ARE-YOU
KNOW-ALL MEN OF
GOOD WILL-

WAIT A MINUTE — BY ALL MEN I MEAN ONLY **THOSE** MEN WHOM WE RECOGNIZE AS WILLING TO BE **REASONABLE** AND SEE OUR SIDE AS WELL AS THEIR OWN — AS LONG AS THEY DON'T HAVE A DOUBLE STANDARD AND PRETEND TO BE NEUTRALISTS.

SO REALLY WHAT THIS DANCE SYMBOLIZES IS A **RESPONSIBLE, CAUTIOUS** APPROACH —

TO ARMS CONTROL
ON EARTH AND
FRUITFUL
NEGOTIATION
TO SOME MEN.

I CALL IT
"THE BENDS."

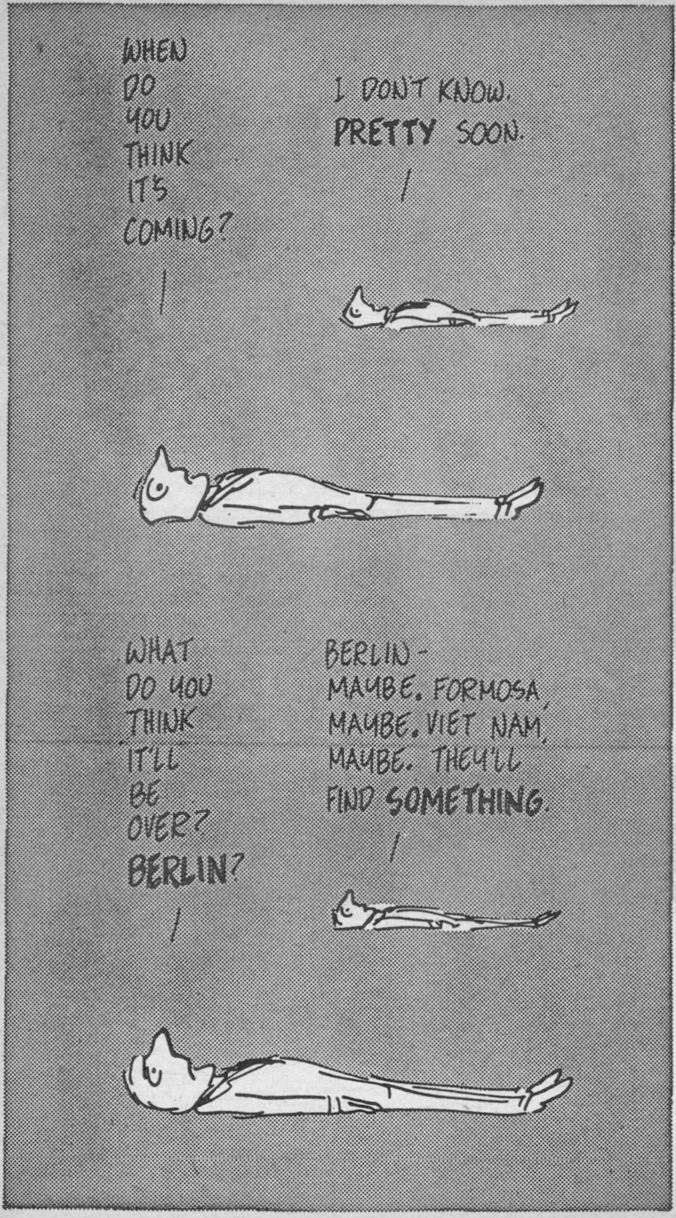

WHEN
DO
YOU
THINK
IT'S
COMING?

I DON'T KNOW.
PRETTY SOON.

WHAT
DO YOU
THINK
IT'LL
BE
OVER?
BERLIN?

BERLIN—
MAYBE. FORMOSA,
MAYBE. VIET NAM,
MAYBE. THEY'LL
FIND **SOMETHING.**

ARE
YOU
GOING
TO
FIGHT?

IT WOULD SEEM
THE PATRIOTIC
THING TO DO.
I HAVEN'T MADE
UP MY MIND.

I'M GOING TO
GO ALONG
WITH OUR
LEADERS.
THEY HAVE
ACCESS
TO INFOR-
MATION **I**
DON'T HAVE.

OBVIOUSLY THEY
MUST KNOW WHAT
THEY'RE DOING.
THEY **ALL** HAVE
DEGREES.

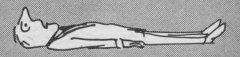

IF THEY SAY FIGHT,
I'LL FIGHT. THE
IDEA OF A DEMO-
CRACY IS THAT
PEOPLE SHOULDN'T
BE **FORCED** INTO
ACTING THE
WAY THE
GOVERNMENT
WANTS.. THEY SHOULD
DO IT ON THEIR **OWN.**

I DON'T CARE SO
MUCH ABOUT ME—
I'VE SINNED. BUT
I DO HOPE THEY
DON'T BLOW UP
THE SEAGRAMS
BUILDING.

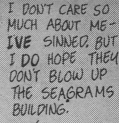

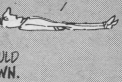

IF THEY
USE THE
NEUTRON
BOMB
THEY
WON'T
EVEN
TOUCH
THE
SEAGRAMS
BUILDING.

THE NEUTRON
BOMB?
WHAT'S THE
NEUTRON
BOMB?

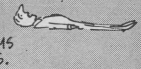

IT ONLY
KILLS
PEOPLE.
IT DOESN'T
HARM
PROPERTY
OR
MACHINES.

DOESN'T HARM
MACHINES, EH?
VERY
ENCOURAGING.

HOW
SO?

THEN MOST
OF US WILL
BE SAFE.

SO BECAUSE IT WAS, YOU
KNOW, MOTHER'S DAY I
SAVED UP ALL MY
ALLOWANCE AND I
GOT, YOU KNOW, MY
MOTHER A PRESENT.

SO ANYHOW SUNDAY IT WAS
MOTHER'S DAY AND I WOKE
UP EARLY TO SUR-
PRISE MY MOTHER
WITH HER PRESENT-

A
DECK
OF
CARDS.

BUT BEFORE I COULD LIKE
DO IT, MY MOTHER SAID—

"YOU ARE THE
REASON THAT I
AM A MOTHER
SO WE ARE
GOING TO
MAKE THIS
YOUR HOLIDAY."

SO MY MOTHER AND MY
FATHER AND ME WENT
TO A BIG ADVENTURE
MOVIE WHICH THEY
SAID I WOULD
ENJOY, CALLED
"HIROSHIMA MON
AMOUR"

AND WE SAT IN THE BALCONY BECAUSE MY MOTHER SAID I COULD SEE BETTER THAT WAY AND ANYHOW SHE COULD SMOKE. THEN WE WENT OUT TO EAT.

AND BECAUSE IT WAS MY CELEBRATION I WAS MADE TO SIT AT THE HEAD OF THE TABLE AND HAD TO CUT MY OWN FOOD AND GOT THE LAMB CHOPS ON THE FLOOR. AND MY MOTHER SAID SEEING HOW IT WAS MOTHER'S DAY, I COULD AT LEAST **TRY**.

THEN WE CAME HOME AND
I STILL DIDN'T GIVE MY
MOTHER HER PRES-
ENT SO I GAVE
HER THE DECK OF
CARDS AND MY
FATHER LAUGHED
AND SAID, "BOY,
THAT'S SURE AS HELL
APPROPRIATE!" SO
THERE WAS A
FIGHT. I THINK,
ABOUT MY FATHER'S
DRINKING.

AND MY
MOTHER
WANTED TO
KNOW HOW
MUCH I
SPENT.

WHY CAN'T
THERE BE
MOTHER'S
DAY IN
THE SUMMER
WHEN I'M
AWAY IN
CAMP.

WHEN I WAS VERY YOUNG I WAS TOTALLY SELF-ORIENTED. I FELT THAT WHEN I ENTERED A CROWDED ROOM I WAS REALLY THE ONLY PERSON THERE.

AND THAT WHEN I LEFT THE ROOM ALL THE PEOPLE BEHIND ME **CEASED** TO EXIST.

THEN AS I GREW A LITTLE OLDER AND
LEARNED DISAPPOINTMENT I DEVELOPED
THE **NEW** FEELING THAT WHEN I ENTERED
A CROWDED
ROOM—

—I WAS THE ONLY PERSON
WHO **WASN'T** THERE.

IN ALL OF LIFE IT SEEMED
TO ME THAT I WAS THE
LEAST REAL

BUT OF COURSE GROWTH
IS A CONTINUING
PROCESS. AS
THE YEARS
WENT BY
I MELLOWED.
I NO LONGER
LOOKED AT
LIFE IN
ABSOLUTES.

I'M NOT SURE ANY
OF US ARE THERE.

WHAT I FIRST
FELL IN LOVE
WITH WAS
YOUR NON-
CONFORMITY.
YOUR CONTEMPT
FOR THE
MATERIAL
VALUES OF
SOCIETY.

WHAT I FIRST
FELL IN LOVE
WITH WAS
YOUR **CALM**-
YOUR ABILITY
TO MAKE
EVERY
EMERGENCY
SEEM ALMOST
NORMAL

WHEN WE FIRST
MARRIED I
LOVED YOUR
REFUSAL TO
SURRENDER
TO THE
MOB-
YOUR
PURITY
OF
MOTIVATION.

WHEN WE FIRST
MARRIED I
LOVED YOUR
SERENITY
FOR THE
WAY IT
ALLAYED MY
DOUBTS -
STRENGTHENED
ME IN MOMENTS
OF **CONFUSION**-

BUT AFTER
HERBERT'S
BIRTH YOU
CHANGED-
YOU BECAME
SELFISH -
UNRELIABLE.

BUT AFTER
HERBERT'S BIRTH
YOU CHANGED-
YOU BECAME
COOL - YOU
BECAME
REMOVED-

YOU REFUSED TO
FACE THE FACTS
OF LIFE. YOU
INSISTED ON
BEING OUT OF
STEP JUST
FOR THE SAKE
OF BEING
NOTICED!

YOU WERE
ALOOF -
NO LONGER
THERE
WHEN I
NEEDED
YOU -

YOU IGNORED
OUR **NEEDS.**
EVERYONE
ELSE HAD
A NICE
HOME.
WE
DIDN'T.

YOU
BECAME
HARD -

OH, I LOVED THAT EARLY ZANY YOU! WHY DID YOU HAVE TO SPOIL IT AND CHANGE?

HOW I COULD LOVE YOU AGAIN IF YOU WERE JUST SERENE LIKE IN THE OLD DAYS.

I HAD JUST GOTTEN A FAT BONUS FOR CREATING A NEW COPY APPROACH FOR OUR BIGGEST CIGARET ACCOUNT- NO DOUBT YOU'VE SEEN IT-

"MORE TAR- MORE NICOTINE - MORE

RISK
IN

FRONTIER

THE CIGARET THAT SEPARATES THE MEN FROM THE BOYS!"

WHEN SUDDENLY IT DAWNED ON ME THAT I HATED MY JOB. YEAR IN AND YEAR OUT WORKING WITH BRIGHT, IMAGINATIVE PEOPLE WHO USED THEIR INTELLIGENCE TO DIG UP **NEW** REASONS WHY THERE WAS NOTHING WRONG WITH THE WAY THEY EARNED AN INCOME.

SO I DECIDED
TO QUIT.

I TOLD MY WIFE AND SHE
SAID-"YOU'RE NOT IN
COLLEGE ANYMORE" AND
I TOLD MY CO-WORKERS
AND THEY SAID-"YOU'LL
GROW UP" AND I TOLD
MY PARENTS AND THEY
SAID-"FACE THE FACTS
AND BE A MAN"

HOW COME ONLY
UNETHICAL
DECISIONS ARE
CONSIDERED
MATURE ?

SO I QUIT. AND I SAT HOME AND TRIED TO FIGURE OUT WHAT I WAS EQUIPPED TO DO THAT WOULD HAVE **SOME** SOCIAL VALUE IN THE WORLD AND **STILL** MAKE ME A LIVING.

AND THE ANSWER WAS **NOTHING.**

IT'S BEEN FOUR MONTHS NOW. OUR MONEY IS RUNNING LOW. PRETTY SOON I'LL HAVE TO GO BACK TO WORK.

BUT THE WAY I SEE IT, EVEN IF I **CAN'T** DO ANYTHING OF VALUE - IF I QUIT ONE JOB EVERY YEAR AND STAY UNEMPLOYED FOR EIGHT OR NINE WEEKS -

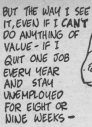

I CAN GO **TWO WHOLE MONTHS** A YEAR WITHOUT DOING **HARM!**

SOME MEN HAVE TO RETIRE BEFORE THEY CAN SAY THAT.

WHEN I GO OUTSIDE AND
LOOK UP AT A CLEAR
BLUE SKY I WANT TO
ENJOY THAT CLEAR
BLUE SKY—

BUT I ALWAYS KNOW
INSIDE MYSELF THAT IF
I **CATCH** MYSELF
ENJOYING IT—THAT
CLEAR BLUE SKY
WILL SUDDENLY
RAIN ON ME.

IF I'M HAVING A WONDERFUL TIME WITH A BOY AND SENSE THAT I'M BEGINNING TO FALL IN LOVE, I **KNOW** THAT IF I **CATCH** MYSELF ENJOYING THE IDEA OF FALLING IN LOVE HE'LL NEVER CALL AGAIN.

IF I ENJOY **ANYTHING** - MY JOB OR **ANYTHING** - AND IF I **CATCH** MYSELF ENJOYING IT - I'LL ALWAYS EITHER MAKE A MISTAKE OR GET FIRED.

SO I WORK AT NOT NOTICING
WHAT'S AROUND ME AND
IF I SUDDENLY FIND
MYSELF ENJOYING SOME-
THING—BEFORE IT CAN GO
WRONG I KNOCK ON WOOD
AND THINK OF THE
WORLD'S TROUBLES.

THERE'S ONLY ONE
TIME IT'S SAFE
TO ENJOY AN
EXPERIENCE—

AFTER
IT'S
OVER.

ALRIGHT. A WEEK AGO I'M ASLEEP IN BED— TWO IN THE MORNING— AND THE **PHONE** RINGS— THE **SEXIEST** VOICE I'VE EVER HEARD!

SHE SAYS HER NAME IS **DARLENE** AND SHE JUST FLEW IN FROM THE COAST AND SHE'S A FRIEND OF A FRIEND AND SHE HAS NO PLACE TO STAY AND CAN I PUT HER UP FOR THE NIGHT.

ALRIGHT. I KNOW **SOMETHING** MUST BE WRONG—BUT I TELL HER TO COME OVER. AN HOUR LATER SHE ARRIVES. **THE MOST BEAUTIFUL GIRL I HAVE EVER SEEN!** AND IN SHE COMES WITH TWO BOTTLES OF BRANDY AND A DOZEN EGGS.

SHE WHIPS UP THE MOST **FABULOUS** BREAKFAST
I'VE EVER TASTED. WE SIT AND TALK FOR
HOURS. SHE'S READ **ALL**
THE BOOKS I'VE READ -
LOVES **ALL** THE MUSIC
I LOVE - THE **BRIGHT-
EST,** MOST **SEN-
SITIVE** GIRL I'VE
EVER KNOWN!

ALONG TOWARD DAWN WE BEGIN TO NUZZLE
A LITTLE. I BUILD A FIRE. SUDDENLY WE'RE
GRABBING EACH OTHER!
WARM? YOU WOULDN'T
BELIEVE IT! AFFECTIONATE?
YOU HAVE **NO**
CONCEPTION!

IT WAS THE LOVELIEST, PUREST EXPERIENCE
I EVER HOPE TO HAVE - A FANTASY COME
TRUE - ME WITH THE
MOST BEAUTIFUL,
DELIGHTFUL GIRL
IN THE WORLD -
AND SHE **LOVES**
ME! SHE LOVES
ME!

ALL MY LIFE PEOPLE
BEEN TELLING ME I
HAVE A MORAL OBLIGATION.

BEFORE THE WAR I
HAD A MORAL
OBLIGATION TO
FIGHT FASCISM.

DURING THE WAR I OWED IT
TO MY COUNTRY TO **JOIN
THE ARMY.**

AFTER THE WAR IT WAS MY **DUTY** TO WORK FOR **PEACE, INTE-GRATION, DECENT HOUSING** AND **BETTER TELE-VISION PROGRAMS.**

SO I CAN'T BE **FOR** SOMETHING BECAUSE IT'S JUST **RIGHT** ANYMORE. I GOT TO BE FOR IT BECAUSE I'D **OWE** SOMEBODY IF I WASN'T.

I FEEL AS IF I'M LIVING IN A MORAL DEBTORS' PRISON.

LIKE EVERYBODY ELSE I WAS
A SOCIALIST WHEN I WAS
IN COLLEGE DURING
THE TWENTIES -
"SOLIDARITY FOREVER"
"ORGANIZE THE WORKERS!"
"OVERTHROW THE GOVERN-
MENT!"

I WAS A LIBERAL WHEN I GOT
OUT OF COLLEGE IN THE
THIRTIES - "NEW DEAL RECOVERY"
"DOWN WITH BOOM AND BUST"
"UP THE C.I.O."

I WAS A COMMUNIST
DURING THE FORTIES-
"UNITED FRONT"
"FREE EARL
BROWDER"
"JAIL THE
TROTSKYITES."

I WAS A DUPE DURING THE FIFTIES - "BUT I DIDN'T REALIZE-" "THEY USED ME-" "I'LL NEVER SIGN ANYTHING AGAIN-"

AND NOW IN THE SIXTIES I'M A CONSERVATIVE- "KEEP RED CHINA OUT OF THE U.N." "OVERTHROW CUBA" "UP BARRY GOLDWATER."

IT'S GOOD TO SEE I'M STILL IN STEP WITH THE COLLEGE KIDS.

"HOW TO WIN ARGUMENTS ON YOUR SUMMER TOUR OF EUROPE" OR **"A GUIDE TO CONVERSATIONAL COUNTERFORCE"**

ENGLAND: WHEN THEY BRING UP HERMAN KAHN, EDWARD TELLER AND NUCLEAR DETERRENCE (85 POINTS), COUNTER WITH ROY WELENSKY, SOUTHERN RHODESIA AND THE CONTINUED SALE OF ARMS TO SOUTH AFRICA. (90 POINTS)

FRANCE: WHEN THEY BRING UP THE C.I.A., CIVIL RIGHTS AND THE RADICAL RIGHT (80 POINTS), COUNTER WITH THE O.A.S., SUPPRESSION OF THE PRESS AND PLASTIC BOMBS. (85 POINTS)

RUSSIA. WHEN THEY BRING UP THE STOCK MARKET, THE DECLINE OF CAPITALISM AND THE CUBAN FIASCO (75 POINTS), COUNTER WITH HUNGARY, FAILING CROPS AND MAO TSE-TUNG. (85 POINTS)

GERMANY: WHEN THEY BRING UP ALLIED INDECISION ON WEST BERLIN (35 POINTS), YOU MAY COUNTER WITH LATENT NAZISM AND THE FEAR OF A NEW HITLER - BUT IT WILL SCORE YOU NO POINTS - THEY HAVE NEVER HEARD OF EITHER.

A FINAL WORD OF ADVICE: THE BEST WAY TO ESCAPE TROUBLE ON YOUR TOUR OF EUROPE IS TO AVOID SPEAKING TO ANYONE WHO UNDERSTANDS ENGLISH.

ALOHA!

I FLED TO FREEDOM FROM EAST GERMANY. DON'T LOOK AT ME THAT WAY. I SAY I DID!

SO I GOT ACROSS THE BORDER AND THE ALLIED OFFICERS SAID, "MAN, WHAT ARE *YOU* DOING?" AND I SAID "YOU CAN SEE PLAIN WELL WHAT I'M DOING. I'M FLEEING TO FREEDOM."

"WELL, MAN, HOW CAN YOU FLEE TO FREEDOM?" THEY ASKED ME. "YOU GERMAN?" AND I REPLIED "NO SIR". "YOU CHINESE?" AND I REPLIED, "NO SIR". "YOU RUSSIAN, HUNGARIAN, ALBANIAN, CZECH, POLE, **SIBERIAN**?" AND TO ALL THAT STUFF I REPLIED "NO SIR." "WELL, THEN", THEY SAID "YOU **CAN'T** BE FLEEING TO FREEDOM."

BUT I WOULDN'T GO BACK SO THEY HAD TO FIGURE OUT WHERE TO SEND ME. THE FRENCH OFFICER SAID "MAN, WE **CAN'T** SEND YOU TO FRANCE. YOU MIGHT GET PICKED OFF AS AN ALGERIAN."

THE ENGLISH OFFICER SAID
"WE ALREADY GOT OUR
TROUBLES IN **LONDON** —
AND SOUTH AFRICA
WOULDN'T HAVE YOU
AND WE AREN'T LIKELY
TO SEND YOU ANY-
WHERES **ELSE** IN
AFRICA BECAUSE FOR
ALL **WE** KNOW YOU
COULD BE A KENYATTA
OR SOMETHING."

AND THE AMERICAN OFFICER
SAID, "WE **CAN'T** SEND
YOU TO THE **SOUTH**
BECAUSE IF YOU
FLED TO FREEDOM
ONCE, WHAT'S TO
STOP YOU FROM
BEING A TROUBLE
MAKER AND TRYING
IT AGAIN?

-AND WE CAN'T SEND YOU TO CUBA BECAUSE THAT'S NO LONGER PART OF THE **FREE WORLD**. THEY REPRESS WHITE FOLKS THERE TOO." SO THEY ALL SAID,"WHY DON'T YOU BE A GOOD FELLOW AND GO BACK WHERE YOU CAME FROM?"

WELL, I DON'T KNOW, MAYBE I WILL. DURING A MORAL CRISIS BETWIXT FREEDOM AND SLAVERY I DON'T WANT TO BE THE ONE TO MAKE TROUBLE.

ALWEEZ S'PLEASH'R
T'BE HERE LAD'Z
AN' GEN'LM'N-
LIKE T'SING
A LI'L SONG I
WROTE 'SPECIALLY
F'YOU-

= snap snap :
snap :

SELLLLLLF PIT PIT PIT-TY PIT-Y! THE WORLD IS FULL OF SELLLLLF PITY- CRYING INTO ITS BEER BECAUSE IT'S SOON LEAVING HERE GOING AWAY OUT **THERE—**

BOOM!

SMASHHHHHHED CIT CIT CIT-TY CIT-Y! ALL WE'LL HAVE IS SMASHHHHHHED CITY- FALLOUT AND MUCH DEBRIS FALLIN' ALL OVER ME OH SAY **CAN** YOU SEE—

BOOM!

IF I GO, YOU GO, WE ALL GO, EARTH.
IF YOU SHOOT, I SHOOT
THEN **WHAT'S** IT ALL WORTH?
A VANISHED PLANET WITHOUT
PRIOR CONSULTATION
IS NO EXAMPLE OF
SELF DETERMINATION —

REFERENNNNNND ME
BEFORE YOU DECIDE
TO **END** ME
GIVE ME A PARTIAL SAY
WE'LL DO IT **YOUR** WAY ANYWAY
THEN WE CAN ALL SALUTE
AND SAY
BOOM!

SO ONE PART OF ME SAID:
"I HATE THIS JOB!
I HATE IT!
I HATE IT!"

THEN ANOTHER PART OF ME SAID:
"REMEMBER YOUR WIFE —
TWO KIDS TO FEED —
HOME IN THE SUBURBS —"

SO ONE PART OF ME SAID:
"I'M STAGNATING! I ONCE
HAD SOME DREAMS! WHAT'S
HAPPENED TO MY LIFE?"

AND THE OTHER PART OF ME SAID:
"WASHING MACHINE
COLOR TV
REPAIRS IN THE ATTIC—"

SO ONE PART OF ME SAID
"IT'S **WRONG** TO SPEND SEVEN
HOURS A DAY AT WHAT I HATE!
IT'S NOT FAIR! IT'S WRONG!"

THEN THE SECOND PART OF ME SAID:
"YOU'RE JUST PENT UP—
GO OUT AND DRINK—
BLOW OFF SOME STEAM—"

AND THAT'S WHY
I SLUGGED YOU.

WHEN I WAS A KID I NEVER COULD UNDERSTAND IT WHEN MY FATHER SHUT HIMSELF OFF IN THE BED-ROOM AND PLAYED SOLITAIRE. MY MOTHER'D ALWAYS SAY "FATHER- **SOME** FATHER- I'M BOTH MOTHER AND FATHER TO THESE KIDS.

THEN, AFTER I GOT MARRIED AND WE HAD KIDS I BEGAN TO SEE IT A LITTLE BETTER. IT'S AS IF MARRIAGE IS FOR THE **MOTHER** AND THE FATHER IS LIKE THE UNCLE WHO VISITS WITH THE **CANDY**- THEY'LL **PLAY** WITH YOU BUT IT'S THE MOTHER WHO **OWNS** THEM. THE FATHER IS ONLY AN UNCLE.

AND WHEN THE KIDS GET OLDER YOU EVEN LOSE THE RANK OF **UNCLE**. THE WIFE SAYS -"I'VE GOT THREE CHILDREN TO TAKE CARE OF- MY HUSBAND AND THE TWO LITTLE ONES. **SOME FAT JOKE.**

SO WHAT HAPPENS WHEN YOU'RE ALMOST FORTY AND TREATED LIKE A LITTLE BOY IN YOUR OWN HOUSE? YOU BEGIN TO **FEEL** LIKE A LITTLE BOY— **THAT'S** WHAT HAPPENS! LIKE **TV**— YOU WANT TO WATCH WHAT **YOU** WANT TO WATCH NOT WHAT **THEY** WANT TO WATCH.

SO YOU START COMING HOME LATER AND LATER. YOU **DRINK** MORE— YOU LEARN HOW TO **BOWL.** AND ALL THE WHILE YOU SAY TO YOURSELF—"HERE I AM THIRTY EIGHT YEARS OLD AND **I** DON'T HAVE IT AS GOOD AS THE **OTHER** KIDS—

—I DON'T EVEN HAVE MY OWN ROOM."

ONE DAY ARNIE, MY HUSBAND, POINTED OUT TO ME THAT EVERY WORD I SAID SOUNDED **EXACTLY** LIKE MY MOTHER.

SO HE SENT ME BACK INTO ANALYSIS AND I WORKED ON IT FOR A YEAR.

BUT WHEN I THOUGHT I WAS BETTER ARNIE, MY HUSBAND, POINTED OUT TO ME THAT EVERY WORD I SAID SOUNDED EXACTLY LIKE MY **FATHER**.

SO HE SENT ME BACK INTO ANALYSIS AND I WORKED ON IT FOR A YEAR.

BUT WHEN I THOUGHT I WAS BETTER ARNIE - HE'S MY HUSBAND - POINTED OUT THAT EVERY WORD I SAID SOUNDED EXACTLY LIKE MY **ANALYST.**

SO HE HAD ME CHANGE ANALYSTS AND I WORKED ON IT FOR A YEAR. AND I WAS SURE I WAS BETTER.

NOW ITS OVER SIX MONTHS AND EVERY WORD I SAY SOUNDS EXACTLY LIKE MY HUSBAND.

ARNIE THINKS I'M CURED.

TO START
WITH I
GOT MY-
SELF A
PARAKEET
WHO WAS
VERY
FRIGHTENED
AT FIRST.

BUT I
TRAINED MY
PARAKEET TO
TRUST ME, TO
LOVE ME, TO
EAT OUT OF
MY HAND.

NEXT I
GOT MYSELF
A CAT WHO
WAS VERY
WITHDRAWN
AT FIRST.

BUT I
TRAINED MY
CAT TO
TRUST ME,
TO LOVE ME,
TO COME
ANYTIME
I CALLED.

NOW I LIVE CONTENTEDLY WITH MY PARAKEET, MY DOG AND MY CAT. WE SPEND EVERY MINUTE OF THE DAY LEARNING TO RELATE. IT'S BEEN AN INVALUABLE EXPERIENCE.

PRETTY SOON I'LL BE READY FOR PEOPLE.